MORE DOG STORIES

The
Basic Vocabulary Series

The books in the *Basic Vocabulary Series* are written with charm of style and high interest appeal for the children. Children love to read them for fun and thus get a vast amount of practice in reading skills. A high literary quality has been maintained in writing these true stories of animals, and retelling tales of folklore.

These Basic Vocabulary books are written with the Dolch 220 Basic Sight Words. The words make up two-thirds or more of all primary reading books and more than half of all other school books. The Dolch 95 Commonest Nouns have also been used. In addition to words from these two basic lists, each book has an average of about one new word per page.

This Series is prepared under the direction of Edward W. Dolch, Ph.D., Professor of Education, Emeritus, University of Illinois. The books in this series are:

Animal Stories	Lion and Tiger Stories
Bear Stories	Lodge Stories
Circus Stories	More Dog Stories
Dog Stories	Navaho Stories
Elephant Stories	Pueblo Stories
Folk Stories	Tepee Stories
Horse Stories	"Why" Stories
Irish Stories	Wigwam Stories

MORE DOG STORIES
IN BASIC VOCABULARY

By

EDWARD W. DOLCH

and

MARGUERITE P. DOLCH

Illustrated by

E. HARPER JOHNSON

GARRARD PUBLISHING COMPANY
CHAMPAIGN, ILLINOIS

LIBRARY OF CONGRESS CARD NUMBER: 62-7208

MANUFACTURED IN THE UNITED STATES OF AMERICA

Foreword

The great interest which was shown for our first book of "Dog Stories" called for this second book of "More Dog Stories." Again, these are all true stories of things which dogs have actually done. The stories have been gathered from experiences of persons, from newspaper and magazine accounts, and from the many books about dogs which their proud masters have written.

Of special interest are the stories about dogs in Alaska, our forty-ninth state. There, dogs drawing dog sleds have played a great part in the development of the country.

These stories tell of how dogs are the companions and friends of both men and women in all their occupations and recreations. There is even an account of how a "seeing-eye" dog saved the life of his master and his mistress, even though the mistress could see.

Many famous writers have devoted whole books to the accounts of their favorite dogs, and there are many other books of true dog stories, told by men and women who loved dogs. It is hoped that the reader will go to these books to find out still more about our good friends, the dogs.

Santa Barbara, California   E. W. DOLCH

List of Pictures

Contents

Dinner Time

He never had a name. He was just called "Dog." Dog did not carry a watch, but Dog could tell time. Dog could not tell what day it was, but Dog knew the day that Train No. 15 stopped.

Train No. 15 goes through a little town in Mississippi at 6:30 in the evening. The train stops a little while and then goes on its way.

Train No. 15 carries a dining car where people sit at little tables and have good things to eat.

The cook on this train liked

dogs. When the train stopped and the cook saw a hungry dog, he always gave the dog something.

One day, the cook saw Dog waiting at the station. Dog always looked hungry, for Dog did not have a home. The cook gave Dog something to eat.

The next day Dog was waiting at the station at 6:30 for Train No. 15. But Train No. 15 did not stop at the little town that day.

The next day Dog was waiting at the station at 6:30. Train No. 15 stopped. Dog was waiting right where the dining car stopped. The cook gave Dog something.

From that day, Dog always waited for Train No. 15. He never went to the station on the days that Train No. 15 did not stop. As soon as the train stopped, Dog was beside the dining car barking and wagging his tail.

The cook would open the little door in his car and say, "Dog, here is your dinner."

For five years, Dog never missed meeting Train No. 15. When the sun was out, Dog was there. When the rain was falling, Dog was there. All the men who worked on the train knew Dog.

One day there was a new cook

on Train No. 15. When the train stopped, Dog was there. He barked and wagged his tail. But the cook did not open his door.

The people who were eating in the dining car looked out of the windows.

"What is the matter with that dog?" they said.

The men who worked on the diner went to the new cook.

"You must give Dog something to eat," they said.

"I have got better things to do," said the new cook.

Dog did not know what had happened to his friend, the cook.

Now all the people on the train wanted to know what was the matter with the dog.

The conductor of the train went to the new cook and said,

"You must give Dog his dinner."

And so the new cook gave Dog his dinner. Then Train No. 15 went on its way.

Dog waited for Train No. 15 for ten years. He was getting to be an old, old dog. Then one day Dog was not waiting at the station of the little town in Mississippi. The men on the train never saw Dog again.

A Funny Helper

Don was a little black and white dog. He lived on a farm. Of all the animals on the farm, Don liked best a big white hen.

At first, Don would run after the hen and bark. But the hen never seemed to be afraid of the little dog. Sometimes Don would take food away from the big white hen. And all the hen would do was to "cluck" at the dog in the most friendly way.

At last, Don and the big white hen became good friends. Don and the hen would sit side by side in the sun.

But one day the hen stayed in the barn. She did not come out to sit in the sun with the little dog. Don looked and looked for his friend. He found her in the barn sitting on a nest of eggs.

Don tried in every way to get the big white hen to play with him. But the hen just sat on her nest.

Since the hen would not come out of the barn, Don stayed in the barn and sat beside the hen. Every day for three weeks, the little dog went to the barn and sat beside his friend.

Then the big white hen had a lot of little chickens. Some of the chickens were white and some were black, and some were yellow. Don liked the little chickens and tried to help the hen look after them.

If one of the little chickens got too far away from the mother, Don would make it go back. He seemed to know that the little chickens should stay with their mother.

When the big white hen took

her little family to the barnyard to hunt bugs, Don went along to help.

The hen cried, "Cluck! Cluck!" and scratched in the dirt. Don watched the chickens hunt for bugs. Then he tried to help.

Don scratched a hole in the ground. The dirt fell on the little chickens and they ran to their mother.

But the mother hen said, "Cluck. Cluck." She took the chickens to the hole that Don had made. They found many bugs. Then Don would scratch another hole for the chickens.

It was very funny to watch the little dog help the mother hen look after her chickens. Don was a good helper.

Ham, for Hamburger

Jerry was a boy who worked at a Drive-in. When a car stopped at the Drive-in and honked, Jerry went out to see if the people in the car wanted a hamburger or drinks. Jerry knew that people did not like to wait for what they wanted. He was always quick to get to the cars.

One day it was raining. There was not much going on at the Drive-in. Jerry was talking to the cook. The cook was making hamburgers for a man and his wife who had just come in out of the rain.

Suddenly, there was the sound of a horn honking outside.

"See what the people want," said the cook.

Jerry put on his raincoat and went out into the rain. He was gone a long time. When he got back he said to the cook,

"I went all around the Drive-in. There was no car there but the car that belongs to these people in here who are eating hamburgers."

Jerry took off his raincoat.

Suddenly a horn honked outside. It honked and honked.

Jerry put on his raincoat and went out. There was only one car outside and that was the car of the people who were eating hamburgers.

Jerry stood and looked around. Suddenly a horn honked. It was the horn of the car that was standing there. The horn honked and honked.

Jerry went and looked into the car. A little dog was honking the horn.

Jerry laughed.

"I guess you want a hamburger," he said.

Just then the man and the lady came out of the Drive-in. The lady was carrying a hamburger. They got into the car. Then they gave the hamburger to the little dog.

"So that is why he honked the horn," said Jerry. "He wanted a hamburger."

"Yes," said the lady, "We call him Ham, for hamburger. We always take him with us in the car. When we stop at a Drive-in for a hamburger, we always have to bring him one."

Jerry went back into the Drive-in. He took off his raincoat. He said to the cook,

"I have just been talking to Ham, a dog. He thinks you make very good hamburgers."

Lost on the Mountain

Eddie was six years old. He loved to go with his mother and her friends to pick berries on the mountain side.

There were no children for Eddie to play with. But he had a big dog that he called Doggie. Eddie and Doggie had a good time playing together.

When it was time to go home, Mother called Eddie. Eddie did not come. Mother and her friends hunted for Eddie. But Eddie and Doggie could not be found.

Mother went home as fast as she could. She told Father that Eddie was lost on the mountain. Father and some neighbors hunted all night for Eddie.

In the night, a bad storm came over the mountain. The wind blew and rain came down. It was such a bad storm that Father and the neighbors who were helping him had a hard time getting home.

"No child could live on the mountain in this storm," said Father. "I am afraid that Eddie is dead."

The wind blew and the rain came down all the next day. Again the men hunted on the mountain, but no one could find Eddie.

Eddie's mother cried all that day.

The next night, the wind and the rain stopped. That morning, two days after Eddie was lost, a hunter came down from the mountain. He was carrying Eddie. And Doggie was walking beside him.

Mother and Father were so happy that they could hardly talk. But after a while, they asked Eddie what happened to him.

"I found a little hole in the rocks

to play in," said Eddie. "Then the rain started. It was cold, but Doggie kept me warm. Then I got hungry and went out and found some berries. I ate a lot of them, but Doggie did not like berries."

"When I found them," said the hunter, "the dog would not let me come near the boy. He barked and growled. But I called to the boy, and he came to me. Then the dog wagged his tail. I gave the boy and the dog something to eat. The dog would not eat anything until the boy had eaten. That dog loves your boy."

Eddie had been out on the mountain two days and two nights with only the dog to look after him.

Doggie was petted by Mother and Father and all the neighbors. And when Eddie met people, he always had to tell how Doggie had looked after him when he was lost on the mountain.

Old Shep and Young Shep

Dogs that look after sheep are very smart dogs. This is the story of two sheep dogs.

One of these sheep dogs was very old. His Master had got a younger dog to help look after the sheep.

The Master told Old Shep that he was to show Young Shep what he was to do. And the old dog seemed to understand.

Old Shep showed the young dog how to look after the sheep. Every day the sheep had to be taken to where the grass was green. When the sun was going down, the sheep had to be brought home again. When the sheep came into the barnyard, Old Shep seemed to know if one was gone, and would go after it.

Sometimes Old Shep and Young Shep took the sheep down the road where cars were going. But the dogs always kept the sheep on the side of the road. No sheep got hurt or were lost when the dogs were looking after them.

Young Shep was a smart dog and learned very quickly. Soon the old dog began to let the young dog do most of the work.

The dogs were fed every day, but now and then the Master gave each dog a big bone with meat on it. When Young Shep had eaten as much meat off his bone as he wanted, he would bury his bone in the ground.

It is hard work to bury a big bone in the ground. So Old Shep did not bury his bones. But when Old Shep wanted a bone, he would dig up the bones Young Shep had buried.

What was Young Shep to do?

One day the Master saw Young Shep burying a bone. He was working very hard and digging a big, big hole. He put his bone in the hole and put some dirt over the bone.

Then Young Shep went away. The Master did not know why Young Shep did this.

Soon Young Shep came back. He had an old bone with no meat on it. The dog put the old bone into the hole and covered it with dirt.

Soon the Master saw Old Shep digging in the hole that Young Shep had made. Old Shep came to the old bone, picked it up and carried it away. He did not know that another bone was still down in the hole.

In this way, Young Shep saved his good bone with meat on it for himself.

Young Shep was a very smart dog.

Porthos, the St. Bernard

Porthos was a St. Bernard. And a St. Bernard is a very big dog. But Porthos never got over wanting to play with toys. When he went for a walk, he always stopped to look into the window of a toy store.

Sometimes Porthos would see a toy that he wanted very much. He would sit down in front of the window and wait. His Mistress would call, "Come, Porthos, come." But Porthos would just sit in front of the toy store window.

His Mistress would have to go into the toy store. The man in the toy store would ask,

"How old is the child for which you want to buy this toy?"

The Mistress did not want to say, "I am buying the toy for that great big dog who is looking into your window."

She would go to the window and point to one toy after another. When she pointed to the right toy, Porthos would bark. And she would buy that toy.

Porthos liked dolls best of all. He learned that dolls came in packages. He learned to open any package he would find. The big dog thought that every package would have a doll in it.

The Master and Porthos had much fun together. They would play at fighting and would fall on the grass. But the big dog never hurt his Master.

Porthos never hurt any living thing. At one time, he caught a bird and brought it to his Mistress. He did not hurt the bird at all. At another time he caught a live rabbit. He carefully made a hole in the ground and put the rabbit into it. But he did not hurt the rabbit.

Porthos helped a mother cat take care of her six kittens. If the kittens got out of their box, Porthos put them back again. The mother cat got tired of staying with her kittens. She would go away. Porthos would go and get the cat and bring her back to the kittens.

One time, Porthos was in a play. The Master had made a play for the children and he made a part in it for Porthos.

In the play, the Mistress took the part of a little girl who went to school. Porthos went to school with her. Of course the Mistress had a little cake in her pocket. Later, she would give the cake to Porthos.

In the play, the Master played the part of a bad man. Porthos had a fight with the bad man. It looked like a fight, but Porthos was only playing at fighting as he had learned to do with his Master.

The children thought the play was wonderful. At the end, Porthos came out with the others. He wagged his tail and barked.

Achilles

Achilles was a big strong dog. He was not afraid to fight any dog. But you had to be careful how you called Achilles.

You had to call Achilles in a kind voice. If you called the big dog in an angry voice, he would not come to you. He would run the other way.

Achilles did not know how strong he was. It was very hard to take a walk with Achilles. His Mistress always said,

"I put Achilles on his leash and

we go for a walk. But Achilles does not walk with me. I go where Achilles wants to go."

If Achilles wanted to go across the street, he just went across the street. He was so strong that his Mistress could not hold him back. And you could never scold Achilles, or he would just run away from you.

One day Achilles and his Mistress were going for a walk. Achilles was walking along very quietly.

Suddenly Achilles saw across the street a little dog barking at a young man. Away went Achilles. He wanted to see this very little dog who was doing so much barking.

Achilles pulled his Mistress across the street so fast that she fell down. She let go of the leash. And she was very angry.

"Achilles, you bad dog! Come here!" said the Mistress.

Away went Achilles down the street as fast as he could go.

The young man said,

"I will get your dog for you." And he ran down the street as fast as he could go.

The Mistress ran down the street as fast as she could go, calling "Achilles, Achilles."

Some little boys who were playing in the street saw her. They ran on down the street after her as fast as they could go to see what was happening.

A policeman in the street saw the young man coming so fast, with the lady running after him. He stopped the young man and wanted to know what was the matter.

The lady came up just then and told the policeman that they were all trying to catch Achilles, the big dog. So the policeman went with them.

Away went the young man and the policeman and the Mistress and the little boys down the street calling, "Achilles, Achilles."

Achilles had been running away, but he met another dog. He did not like this dog, and he stopped and growled. The dog growled too. And all at once there was a dog fight.

Just then the young man and the policeman and the Mistress and the little boys came up.

The Mistress knew that Achilles did not know how strong he was. He could hurt the other dog very badly.

The young man and the policeman were trying to get Achilles away from the dog. But Achilles would not stop fighting.

Then the Mistress went up to the two fighting dogs. Her voice was very kind.

"Achilles, my dear Achilles," she said. "Come, my little pet. Good Achilles. Come to me."

Everyone stopped. Everyone looked. They all started to laugh.

They had never seen anyone try to stop a dog fight like that.

But Achilles heard his Mistress. She was calling him "Good dog," in her kindest voice.

Achilles always thought of himself as a very "good dog." He let go of the other dog and came to his Mistress right away.

Jokko

Two old ladies lived in a little white house. Mary was the older. She could not hear at all, but her quick eyes took in everything around her. Ruth was also getting so that she could not hear. She knew that before long she would not hear anything.

Ruth did not know what two old ladies would do when they could not hear. They did not have enough money to have someone look after them. And they did not want to leave their little white house in which they had lived so many years.

A kind man named Mr. Jones lived next door to the two old ladies. Mr. Jones trained dogs. One day he said to Ruth,

"I think that you and Mary need a dog to look after you."

Then Ruth told Mr. Jones that she was afraid that she could not tell when the door bell rang.

Mr. Jones said,

"I will train Jokko to tell you when the door bell rings."

Jokko was trained to bark when

the door bell rang. He went to live with the two old ladies.

Mary and Ruth were very happy. Jokko was a good helper. He would tell them if anyone was at the door. If he heard the bell, he would come and stand in front of them and bark. Then they would go to the door.

One day Jokko barked and barked. Ruth went to the door, but no one was there. Still Jokko barked and barked. He went first to Ruth and then to Mary.

"I do not know what Jokko wants," said Ruth.

"He is trying to tell us something," said Mary. "You had better go and get Mr. Jones. He will know what Jokko wants."

When Mr. Jones came, Jokko barked in front of him. Then he ran to the cellar door and barked and barked.

"He wants me to go down in the cellar," said Mr. Jones.

Mr. Jones went down into the cellar. And there he saw that a gas pipe was broken.

No one could have told that the pipe was broken because the gas did not have much smell. But it could be smelled by the nose of a dog.

The two old ladies would have died that night if Jokko had not told them about the gas in the house.

"Jokko has saved your lives," said Mr. Jones.

The Dog and the Farmer

One winter a little black and white dog came to a farm in Canada. No one wanted the little dog. But the farmer let him stay in the barn.

One day, when the snow covered everything, the farmer had to go to town. He had to get some hay for his animals.

The farmer put a hayrack on a sled. A hayrack is a kind of big box for hay. There were two big horses to pull the sled. The farmer stood in the hayrack and drove the horses.

The wind was blowing very hard. The snow was blowing so the farmer could not see where he was going. But the farmer was sure that the horses would find the way to town.

The wind began to blow harder. It blew so hard that suddenly the hayrack went off the sled. The farmer found himself in the snow, with the hayrack over him. He was just like in a box, and he could not get out.

The farmer tried and tried to

make a hole in the side of the hayrack. But the boards were too strong for him. He could not break them.

The farmer was still near the farm house. He called and he called. But no one heard him.

The cold was making the farmer sleepy. He knew that if he went to sleep, he would freeze. So he called and called.

At last, the farmer looked between the boards of the hayrack and saw a little dog come running over the snow. It was the dog that stayed in the farmer's barn.

The dog came up to the hay-rack that was over the farmer. He barked and barked. Then the little dog seemed to know just what to do.

The dog started to chew a hole in one of the boards. He chewed and he chewed. At last he had made a hole in the board.

The farmer kept saying, "Good dog. Good dog." When the hole was big enough for the farmer to get his hand into it, he found that he could break the board. Then the farmer could get out through the place where the board had been.

The farmer was so cold that he could hardly walk. He wanted to sit down and rest. But the little dog would not let the farmer sit down. So the farmer kept on walking toward the farm.

At last the farmer got home. The dog had saved his life. Now the little dog has a home. He lives with the farmer and his wife.

Almo

Almo was a seeing-eye dog. He had been trained to look after his Master, who was blind. When the Master left the house, Almo went with him. He kept his Master on the sidewalk. He took his Master across streets. He took care of his Master at all times.

Almo and his Master and the Master's wife were staying on the top floor of a small hotel. They were resting in the afternoon, for that night the Master was to give a talk on the work of seeing-eye dogs.

Almo could not keep still. He walked up and down the room. Then he came to the side of his Master's bed and put his cold nose on the Master's face.

The Master knew that something was the matter.

The Master put the harness on Almo and took him into the hall. Everything seemed to be all right.

The Master told Almo to go back to the room. Almo did not want to go back. But he obeyed.

The Master started to take the

harness off Almo, but Almo barked and barked and pushed his Master toward the door. The Master did not know what to do.

At last, the Master called his wife who had been sleeping. His wife could see and so she could find out what was the matter.

Now all three went out into the hall. The Master smelled smoke at once.

His wife said, "The hall is full of smoke. I cannot see anything."

The Master could hardly breathe because of the smoke. He heard people callng, "Fire! Fire!"

He knew that his wife's eyes could not help. So he called to Almo, "To door outside."

The dog went down the hall through the smoke. The Master had hold of the harness and the wife had hold of the Master's arm.

Suddenly Almo stopped and barked. The Master put out his hand. They had come to a window.

"Almo has brought us to the fire escape," he said to his wife. He opened the window.

The Master wanted Almo to go out first. "Outside," he said. But Almo would not go. Then the Master knew that Almo would not leave him. So the Master climbed through the window and out on to the part of the fire escape before the window. Almo went with him. Then the wife climbed out.

Now they could breathe.

The fire escape went down to a roof. Firemen were on the roof. They were calling to the people on the fire escape.

The Master climbed down the fire escape. It did not go all the way to the roof. So when the Master came to the end of it he fell the rest of the way. But he was not hurt.

Firemen went up the fire escape

and got the Master's wife. Almo was left up on the fire escape.

The Master's wife knew that Almo could not come down the fire escape. So she told two firemen how to pick up the big dog.

"Put one arm under him just back of his front legs. Put another arm under him at his back legs. Then you can carry him without hurting him."

A fireman went up the fire escape. He picked up Almo and carried him down to the roof.

The firemen were calling from the ground for the people to get off the roof near the fire. So the firemen took the Master and his wife and Almo across the roofs to where they would be away from the fire.

The Master and his wife were saved because Almo found his way through the smoke to a window where the fire escape was.

The Captain's Dog

The "Elsie," a big ship, was carrying many men, women and children. A storm was blowing up at sea. Then something broke in the ship. The Captain could not steer the ship any more.

The high winds blew the ship toward the shore. Near the shore were great rocks that would break the ship to pieces. Everyone on the steamer would be lost.

On the shore, people stood in the storm and rain. The ship was not far from the shore. But no one could get out to the ship, for the waves were too high.

The people on the shore got a big gun that fired a big ball with a rope on it. If they could shoot the ball over the ship, the men on the ship could get the rope. Then they could pull the rope and get hold of a bigger rope that was tied to it. They could tie the big rope to the ship. Then a basket could be pulled out to the ship to take off the men, women and children.

Again and again, the men on the shore fired the gun. But the wind was blowing so hard that they could not get the big ball to go over the ship. The rocks and the high waves were beginning to break up the ship.

The Captain of the "Elsie" had a big black dog that always was with him. The dog seemed to know that something was happening to the ship. He ran up and down and barked and barked. The Captain had a thought.

"Come here," said the Captain to the big dog. "Maybe you can save us. A man cannot get through those waves. Maybe a dog can."

The Captain tied a rope to the dog's collar. Then he said,

"Swim to the shore, boy. Swim to the shore."

The big dog jumped into the water. The big waves pushed him this way and that. But he kept on swimming.

The people on the ship stood and watched the dog. The people on the shore saw the dog too, and they stood and watched.

Sometimes the people could see the big black head of the dog as he was swimming in the water. Sometimes the waves would break over the head of the dog, and he would be gone. But then he would come up again, still swimming.

As the big dog got near the shore, the people were afraid that he would be thrown on the rocks and be killed.

Some men on the shore tried to get out into the water to help the dog. But the waves drove them back.

As the dog got nearer the shore the people saw that he was so tired that he could hardly swim. Then a big wave broke over his head and he went down.

The men on the shore went again into the water to save the dog. They got to him. They pulled him to the shore. The big dog lay on the shore, trying to breathe.

The men on the shore quickly took the rope from the dog's collar. They tied a big rope on to the end of it. And the Captain and his men pulled and pulled and got the big rope to the ship.

It did not take long to get the big basket going from the ship to the shore. It was blown by the winds but it went right over the great high waves. The basket got

all of the men, women and children
to the shore.

The big black dog had saved
them.

Don, the "Lion Dog"

Don was a "lion dog" who belonged to Jones. Jones was a man who lassoed mountain lions and sent them to zoos.

Jones had a lot of dogs who were trained to find a mountain lion and drive him up a tree.

"That Don is the smartest dog that I have," said Jones. "He is always way ahead of the other dogs. And he is not afraid to go after a lion by himself. One of these days a lion is going to turn on him. And that will be the end of a good lion dog."

The other dogs looked to Don as a leader. He was the first to find the smell of the lion. He followed it, and the other dogs raced after him. Don was the first to find out that the lion had climbed a tree. The other dogs stood around the tree and barked and barked. Then Jones and his helpers came up on their horses. They lassoed the mountain lion and tied it so that it could not get away.

Don did not like the other dogs. He kept away from them. Don did not like the men. Men had not been kind to him. He did not trust them. Don did his work as a lion dog. He ate by himself. He liked to sleep by himself.

One day a mountain lion almost killed Don. Don had found the smell of the lion. He ran ahead of the other dogs. He found the lion, and the lion jumped up into a tree. The tree was only a small tree and it broke. The lion fell to the ground.

By the time the other dogs got to the tree, there was a hard fight going on between Don and the lion. The lion bit Don in the neck and Don lay on the ground almost dead.

The other dogs ran into the

fight. One dog bit the lion in the back leg. When the lion turned on him, another dog bit the lion in the back legs. The lion was very angry.

When the men came up on their horses, they had to shoot the lion or he would have killed some of the dogs.

Then the men saw Don on the ground.

"I knew some lion would get Don," said Jones. "He never would wait for the rest of the dogs to come up and help him."

Jones carried Don to a tree where there was still some snow

on the grass. Jones put snow in his handkerchief and put the handkerchief and the snow on the dog's neck where the lion had bit him. Then Jones tied his scarf around the dog's neck. He put a ball of snow beside the dog so that Don could get some water if he wanted some.

Don lay on the grass as if he were dead.

"I always knew a lion would get Don sooner or later," said Jones to the other men as they went back to camp. They could not move Don. He was too badly hurt.

It rained all the next day, and

the men and dogs did not go hunting lions. The men sat around the camp. They talked about Don and what a good lion dog he had been.

"I will have to go back and bury Don," said Jones, "he was a good lion dog."

The next day the rain had stopped. The men were getting ready for the day's hunt.

Then out of the woods came Don. He could hardly walk, but he was coming into camp.

"It is Don," said Jones. And he ran towards the dog.

It was Don with the scarf still

tied around his neck. He was a very sick dog, but he had found his way back to camp.

"Don, you old lion dog, how did you ever get back?" said Jones.

Don looked at Jones. And then for the first time in his life, he wagged his tail at a man. Don had found a friend.

Scruffy, a Movie Dog

One day a puppy got lost. He was picked up and taken to the Home for Lost Dogs. No master came to get the puppy. So he grew up in the Home.

One day a man and a lady came to look at the dogs in the Home. When the lady saw this dog, she said,

"That is the dog we want for the movie. He is so scruffy."

And that is how Scruffy got his name.

Scruffy's Master worked in the movies. Scruffy tried to do everything his Master told him to do. He liked his Master very much.

In a movie, the Master could not speak to Scruffy. So the Master taught Scruffy to obey when he moved his hand. So Scruffy would sit or stand or come or bark when the Master told him to with his hand.

One day the Master heard that a dog was needed for a part in a very big movie. The Master knew that Scruffy would be a very good dog for the part.

The Master was sure that if he could get the director of the picture to see Scruffy, he would let Scruffy play the part.

The Master took Scruffy to the door of the director's office. He put out his hand and Scruffy knew that he was to "stay." Scruffy stayed by the door of the director's office all day.

Everyone who went by the office stopped to talk to Scruffy.

"What a fine dog," they said. "He would be a good dog to have in a movie."

But the director of the picture

did not see Scruffy. The director was home, sick in bed.

Later on the Master brought Scruffy down to the director's office again. But he could not see the director right away.

Just then, the Master went away from the door to talk with friends. He did not see that Scruffy did not go with him.

Scruffy sat beside the door of the director's office. When someone came out of the office, Scruffy went in.

There was a man looking at some papers. He did not see Scruffy.

"Shut the door," said the man. Scruffy, who knew how to shut doors, shut the door. Then he went and sat beside the man. But the man still did not see him.

"Wait just a minute," said the man, "until I look over this paper."

Scruffy sat still. His Master had taught him to be still and quiet when he was told to "wait."

"Did you bring that paper?" asked the man. And the man put out his hand, without looking up.

Scruffy knew what to do when someone put out his hand. Scruffy put his paw in the man's hand.

The man was so surprised to

find a paw in his hand that he jumped out of his chair.

"How did you get in here?" said the man.

Scruffy barked. And then he sat up and begged.

"Down," said the man.

Scruffy lay down on the floor beside the man.

There was a knock on the door.

"Still," said the man. Scruffy did not make a sound.

"Come in," said the man.

The Master came in.

"I heard that you need a good dog for the new movie," said the

Master. "I think that I have just the dog that you want."

"I already have the dog I want," said the director. "You must see him. He is just the right dog for the part."

"Come here," said the director. And Scruffy came out from behind the chair.

And that is how Scruffy got the part.

Woof

Woof was a very little dog with a very big bark. Woof was so little that he could ride in the pocket of his Master's great coat.

The Master went to Alaska to take pictures of animals, and he took Woof along. They went to live with an Old Man in a little house in the woods. When the Old Man saw Woof he laughed and laughed.

"What a dog to bring to Alaska," he said. "We have big dogs in Alaska."

In the little house and in the woods, there were many new things for Woof to see and to smell.

At night, Woof could hear the bears growling as they fished in the river near the little house. But Woof was not afraid of bears.

One morning Woof and his Master went to the river. The Master wanted to take pictures of bears. A bear was fishing, and the Master wanted to take his picture.

But Woof had never seen a bear before. He ran right up to the bear and barked and barked and barked.

The bear was sure that all animals would run away from him. But Woof didn't run away. He barked and barked.

The bear looked at the dog. The bear growled. The dog barked. Then the bear turned and walked away.

One day Master and Woof found a beaver working on a beaver dam. The beaver was making the dam higher. Woof had never seen a beaver before. He ran out on the dam. But he fell into the water, and Master had to go out and pull him out. He put Woof in his pocket and then took some pictures.

The greatest fun that Woof had was trying to catch a salmon. There were many salmon going up the river. There was a place where the salmon had to jump over some sand. Sometimes a salmon would jump but come down on the sand.

Woof would run out on the sand and try to hold on to the salmon by the tail. Woof pulled and pulled. But the salmon was so big and strong that it would pull Woof right into the river.

Then Woof would let go of the

salmon and try to get back to the sand. Sometimes the Master had to come and get him out of the river.

The Old Man who lived in the little house thought that Woof's fights with the salmon were very funny.

"That little dog is not afraid of anything," he said.

And the Old Man would give Woof some good things to eat.

Lady

Lady belonged to Miss Jarvis. Lady and Miss Jarvis lived in an old house in a little town. Everyone in the town knew Miss Jarvis. And everyone in this town knew Lady.

Miss Jarvis was quite old, but every afternoon she went for a walk with Lady. Miss Jarvis walked slowly, but Lady ran up and down. One day, as they were going across a street, a car hit Lady.

Lady was badly hurt. The man

in the car took Lady and Miss Jarvis to the veterinarian, or a dog-doctor.

Dr. Ford was a good dog-doctor. He took good care of Lady, and she got well.

Miss Jarvis was very happy to have her dog well again. She had been very much afraid when Lady was hit by the car.

"Lady," said Miss Jarvis, "I will have to take care of you. I will have to put a leash on you when we go for our walk in the afternoon."

Lady did not like to walk on a leash. She would pull and pull. And little Miss Jarvis had a hard time keeping up with her. But every afternoon they took their walk.

One day Lady was playing in the back yard of the old house. She found something to eat in the yard. It was something that made her sick. And when dinner time came Lady did not want to eat anything.

"What is the matter, Lady?" said Miss Jarvis. "You are always hungry for your dinner."

Lady just drank a little water. Then she asked to go outside.

After a time, Miss Jarvis went to the door and called,

"Lady, Lady, come in."

But Lady did not come. It began to get dark. Miss Jarvis called "Lady, Lady," again and again. But Lady did not come.

Miss Jarvis thought of how the car had hit Lady. She was afraid that Lady had been hurt again.

Miss Jarvis went and asked the neighbors if they had seen Lady. But no one had seen Lady. Miss Jarvis came back to her own house and waited. Where was Lady? What had happened to her? How could she be found?

At last Dr. Ford, the veterinarian, called up.

"Is this Miss Jarvis?" said the Doctor. "I just want to tell you that Lady is with me. She came to my door and barked. When I let her in, she seemed to be sick. So I gave her some medicine and put her to bed. She will be all right in the morning."

"Lady is a smart dog," said Miss Jarvis. "She was sick and she went to the doctor to make her well. Thank you, Dr. Ford, for looking after my dog."

Pierrot

Pierrot was a white dog who fooled his Master. Pierrot was very smart.

Pierrot may have thought that it was all right to fool his Master. His Master sometimes fooled him.

Pierrot liked to play with a little white ball. His Master would throw the ball and Pierrot would go and find it. But the Master liked to fool Pierrot. He would throw with his arm but he would not let go of the ball. Then he would put the ball into his pocket. Pierrot would hunt and hunt. But he could not find the little white ball. The Master thought this was fun. But Pierrot did not think it was fun.

One day the cook was making two chickens ready for dinner. She put the chickens on the table and went away for a minute. When she came back, one of the chickens was gone. She could not find the chicken anywhere.

Who could have taken the chicken from the table?

The cook went to the Master

to tell him what had happened. Pierrot was sleeping in a chair.

"I think that Pierrot took a chicken from the table," said the cook. The Master looked at Pierrot in the chair.

"Pierrot," said the Master, "did you take a chicken from the cook's table?"

Pierrot opened his eyes. He jumped from the chair. He was very sleepy. His eyes seemed to say,

"Why did you wake me? Do you want to play ball?"

"Pierrot," said the Master, and

this time his voice was very hard. "Did you take a chicken from the cook's table?"

This time Pierrot hung his head.

"Look at him," said the cook. "I know that he took the chicken. But what did he do with it?"

"Pierrot," said the Master, "where is the chicken?"

Pierrot did not move. He only hung his head.

The Master wanted to be sure that Pierrot had taken the chicken. The Master went to the kitchen and got the other chicken. He called Pierrot to him.

"Pierrot," said the Master. "Here is a chicken for you." Pierrot did not want to take the chicken but the Master made the dog take the chicken in his mouth.

The Master had never given Pierrot a chicken before. The dog knew that something was the matter. He did not know what to do with the chicken. Slowly Pierrot went out into the garden, carrying the chicken in his mouth. The Master watched to see what he would do with the chicken.

Pierrot put the chicken on the ground and began to dig a hole.

Just as the dog was going to put the chicken in the hole, the Master said,

"Pierrot, let me see what you have in that hole."

In the hole the Master found the first chicken that Pierrot had taken.

"Pierrot," said the Master, "you are a bad dog to take the chicken from the table. What am I to do with you? You must never take a chicken again."

The Master went and got some feathers from the chickens. He tied them on a stick.

When Pierrot asked the Master to play ball, the Master would show him the chicken feathers. Pierrot would hang his head. And they would not play ball.

At last the Master said, "Pierrot, I think that you will never take a chicken again. Now let us play ball. I will throw the little white ball for you. But I will never try to fool you again."

Rex, a Police Dog

Rex was one of the first dogs to help policemen catch robbers. Rex lived in London, England. He was trained by his Master, Arthur Holman, who was a policeman. Arthur Holman was a very good dog trainer too.

Rex learned to "heel," to "sit," to "speak" and to "come." He learned what "good dog" meant. And most of all, he learned "no."

Rex could "track." One time a father could not find his little girl. He called the police and told them his little girl was lost. The police took Rex to help them find the girl.

Rex smelled a dress that the little girl had used. Then he was told to "track." Rex started off into the little town where the girl lived. He followed the "smell" that he found along the way.

Rex stopped to look into the windows of a toy store. He stopped at a candy store. Then he went back to the house where the little girl lived and stopped at the back door.

The police thought that Rex had made a mistake so they tried again. Again they had Rex smell the dress. Again he went to the candy store and the toy store. Again he came back to the back door of the man's house.

The police did not know what to think. They thought that maybe Rex was fooling them. Then one policeman asked the father if he had looked for the little girl in the house. The man went in and found the little girl sleeping in her bed.

At another time, a lady who

had been taking a walk had her purse taken. The man who took it ran away. The police took Rex to the place where this had happened. Rex had been taught to "fetch," which means "get." Rex's Master told him to "fetch."

Rex looked all around on the ground. He brought his Master a button that had been pulled from a raincoat.

That night, the police found a man in the streets with a raincoat that had lost a button. The button that had been found had come from that raincoat. The man said that as he ran away with the purse his raincoat had caught on something. The button had come off.

So Rex had helped catch the robber.

To Catch a Robber

The police would call Rex and his master at any time of the day or night. Many of the calls were at night. Men cannot see at night, but a dog can "track" at night by smelling.

On a Sunday evening Rex was called to help the police.

A neighbor had seen two men leaving a house carrying sacks that were full of something. The neighbor knew that the man who lived in the house was away. So the neighbor called the police.

When Rex got to the house, he picked up the smell of the robbers. Away he went through the garden and down the street. The policemen could not keep up with him. Then they heard him barking.

When the policemen came up to Rex, they found that he was barking at a car that stood at the side of the street. In the car, the policemen found the things that had been taken from the house.

Arthur Holman, Rex's Master, told Rex to "find them." Then he took Rex all around the automobile. Rex went on down the road. At last he stopped at a bus stop, and sat down and barked. He was telling his Master that the robbers had got on the bus. So Rex could not smell them any more.

The robbers seemed lost. The police did not know what to do. But just then the police were told that a man in the next town had said his car had been stolen. And it was the same car that the robbers had used. And the next town was the one to which the bus must have gone.

Arthur Holman was a good policeman. He thought,

"Something is not right about

this. I am going to the next town and see this man." So he told the police of the next town to keep this man until he came.

Arthur Holman took Rex with him to the next town, but he did not take Rex with him into the police station to see the man.

The man told Arthur Holman that he had been in a picture show and that when he came out, he found that his car was gone. Arthur Holman looked at the man's hands. They were very dirty. Arthur Holman did not think that a man would go to the picture show with such dirty hands. So he called for Rex.

As soon as Rex came into the police station, he ran at the man. He knew that the man's smell was the smell of the robbers that he had tracked.

The man was afraid of Rex, and he told the police that he was one of the robbers. He had thought if he said his car was stolen they would never think he had used it for the robbery.

Nick, the Sheep Dog

Nick was a black sheep dog. He was little for a dog that drives sheep, but he would be called a big dog if he were a pet in town. Nick helped his Master and the other sheep dog, Rock, herd sheep out in the mountains of Arizona.

One day, the Master bought a big herd of sheep from the Indians in Arizona. He wanted to take the sheep up into the hills where there was good grass. The sheep would grow and grow. Later on, the Master could sell them for more money.

After the Master bought the sheep, he found there were goats in with the sheep. The Master had not bought the goats. So the goats had to be taken out of the herd of sheep.

This work was done by Nick and Rock. They picked out the goats one at a time. They ran the goats through a gate into another yard. Soon the goats were all out.

The dogs began to drive the herd. For a long day, the herd was driven up into the hills of Arizona.

The Master was heading for a water hole, for sheep cannot go too long without water to drink. When they got to the water hole, there was no water in it.

While the herd was resting, some of the sheep smelled water. Five of them started off toward the smell of water. They left the rest of the herd and headed right for a river.

Nick started out after the five sheep, but the sheep got to the river first.

The river was full of water and was going fast. The fast water carried the sheep down the river. One sheep got out on a rock that was in the river. Nick knew that the sheep would just stay there. So Nick knew that he must swim out to the rock. He climbed the rock and pushed the sheep off of it.

Then Nick jumped into the river again after the sheep. He got them out of the water. He drove them away from the river.

This time, the five sheep went up a deep canyon, with steep sides. They could not climb the sides. They got up on some rocks and could not turn around. They did not know how to go on and they did not know enough to go back.

Nick had to climb up on the rocks. He got through the sheep and got ahead of them. Then he made them turn around. Nick got the sheep to go down from the rock.

At last Nick saw a place where they could get out of the canyon. He drove the sheep up this place. Now they were out of the canyon. Nick drove them toward the grassy hills higher up.

The sheep came to another deep canyon that had a bridge across it. But there was a gate. Nick knew this bridge. He had got sheep over it before. But the Master was not there to open the gate. So Nick opened the gate himself. He took the end of the gate with his teeth. Then he pulled it back. The sheep went over the bridge.

As Nick drove the sheep along, they came to some high rocks. From the top of the rocks, a mountain lion jumped down on one of the sheep. The others ran away. But Nick ran up and barked and barked.

The mountain lion had been hunted. He knew that a barking dog meant more dogs and men with guns. The mountain lion turned and ran. The sheep that the lion had hit was hurt and could not keep up with the other sheep.

Nick got four of the sheep back to the Master and the herd. But he knew one was left. So he went back to get it. It was the sheep that had been hurt by the lion. Nick bit the sheep again and again to keep it going. At last he got that sheep back to the herd.

The Master gave Nick some food. He told Nick he was a good dog. But Nick was just doing what any good sheep dog knew had to be done. Nick knew that his Master's sheep must be kept together.

Pickpocket

There was once a little puppy that no one wanted. His brothers and sisters were big and strong. They grew and grew. They all went to good homes, for people wanted strong puppies. But no one wanted the littlest puppy.

The littlest puppy followed people along the street of his town. He wanted to find someone who would give him a good home. But no one wanted the littlest puppy.

One day the puppy went into Mother Murphy's store. Mother

Murphy was very kind and she let the littlest puppy sleep in the store. After that, the puppy thought that he belonged to Mother Murphy. He made Mother Murphy's store his home.

The puppy grew up to be a good looking dog. But he was never very big. He had a good home, and he liked to show how much he loved Mother Murphy. But he still followed people along the streets of his town.

One day the dog followed a little boy into a candy store. The boy gave the man a quarter and asked the man for ten cents worth of candy. The man gave the boy the candy and a nickel and a dime change. The boy put the change in the pocket of his coat, and went out of the store.

The boy went down the street, eating the candy. The dog followed him. He begged and begged, but the boy would not give him any candy.

Then the dog jumped up and got his nose into the boy's pocket. He got the nickel and dime in his mouth. Then he ran as fast as he could to the candy store. He put the money on the floor and wagged his tail.

The man in the candy store had been standing in the door of the store watching the boy and the dog.

"You little pickpocket," said the man. "The boy would not give you any candy, and so you took the money out of his pocket."

The man took the dime off the floor and gave the dog some candy. The dog sat on the floor and ate all the candy. Then the dog picked up the nickel and ran home to Mother Murphy.

The man at the candy store told other men about the dog who was a pickpocket. The men all laughed at the joke. They called the dog Pickpocket.

Pickpocket still followed men on the street. But now he begged for money. For Pickpocket had found out that he could buy what he wanted with money.

The men thought this was all great fun. They would give Pickpocket some money to see what he would do with it. Sometimes he would go to the butcher and put a dime on the floor. The butcher would give him some meat. He would take his money to buy cake from the grocer. With money he could buy candy at the candy store.

The men would give the little dog a quarter and a dime and a nickel, to see what he would do. Pickpocket would carry the money in his mouth. He would go to the store where he wanted something and put the money on the floor. But he would only let the man take one piece of money. And if the man took the quarter, Pickpocket would bark until he got his change.

Pickpocket would sit in the store and eat what he got. Then he would pick up his change and run home to Mother Murphy. Mother Murphy put a little box beside Pickpocket's bed. Pickpocket kept his money in this box.

Sometimes the men on the street would not give Pickpocket any money when he begged. They wanted to see if he would go to Mother Murphy's and get some money out of his box. But Pickpocket never took money out of that box. It was money he had given to Mother Murphy. It was for her to use.

Mother Murphy was getting very old. One day she got sick and had to go to bed. There was no one to look after her but Pickpocket. Mother Murphy would write on a paper and give the paper to Pickpocket. The dog would take it to a neighbor, who would do what was asked.

The butcher brought meat to Mother Murphy. He would take his money out of Pickpocket's box. The grocer would bring bread and eggs. He would take his money out of Pickpocket's box. When the doctor came to see Mother Murphy, he would take his money out of Pickpocket's box too.

Pickpocket looked after Mother Murphy until she died. Then many people wanted to give Pickpocket a home. But he would not leave Mother Murphy's store. He lived there until he died.

Snowbird

Two men named Black Luke and Beaver lived in Alaska. They were fur trappers. In the winter they went to their traps over the snow on snowshoes. The snow was very deep, but the snowshoes let the men walk right on top of the snow.

One evening Black Luke and Beaver were going back to their camp. It was snowing so hard that they could hardly see to find their way.

Suddenly, the men heard a dog

crying. They knew from the sound that something was wrong. They rushed to where the cry came from and found that a big wolf was fighting a black dog. Black Luke killed the wolf, but the wolf had hurt the dog very badly.

When the men got to the dog, they found that it was a mother dog. She was hurt very badly, but she knew that the men were friends. She took them to where, in the snow, there were two puppies. One puppy was white, and one puppy was black.

The mother had been fighting to save her puppies from the wolf. But she knew that the men were friends and the puppies would be taken care of. She lay down in the snow and she was so badly hurt that soon she was dead.

Black Luke and Beaver took the puppies to their camp. The puppies were so small that their eyes were not open. The men had some frozen milk, and they fed the puppies. They kept the puppies very warm.

Day by day, the puppies grew

and grew. The white puppy was called Snowbird. The black puppy was called Blacky. Both of the big trappers loved the dogs. They loved to play with Snowbird and Blacky. They were very happy to have the puppies.

The two men had to do their work every day. They had to go and see their traps. They had to move from one camp to another. It was hard to take good care of the puppies, and to feed them and keep them warm.

Black Luke and Beaver had a small sled that they pulled themselves. But they could not put the puppies on the sled. They would be too cold. So the men made little hammocks for the puppies. They hung these hammocks under their coats.

Black Luke carried Snowbird and Beaver carried Blacky. Each man had a puppy in a hammock in front of him, under his coat. The coat would keep the puppy warm, and would keep the puppy from putting his head out and getting it cold. But the puppies were heavy.

At last the men got to the camp which was near an Eskimo village. The Eskimos came out to see the puppies. Snowbird was all white, with blue eyes. Blacky had big brown eyes like his mother. The Eskimos looked and looked at them.

Snowbird and Blacky grew to be big strong dogs. Black Luke and Beaver taught them to pull a sled. In Alaska at that time, the only way to get from place to place was by sled. A sled pulled by dogs could go through woods and along rivers.

Black Luke and Beaver made a small sled that was pulled only by their two dogs. But most sleds were larger. Some men would make big sleds that needed many dogs to pull them over the snow. Good sled dogs would bring a lot of money.

One day, Black Luke and Beaver thought that they would go over the mountains to find the Yukon river. They were told they could not do it, but they wanted to try. So they started.

For many days the two men and their sled with the two dogs went higher and higher into the mountains. The wind blew and blew. They got very tired. Their food was all gone. The way was much longer than the men had thought.

Snowbird went on and on, but Blacky was not strong enough. He could not go on pulling the sled. He could not go on without food. And so he died right up near the top of the mountains.

The sled, pulled now by Snowbird alone, went on and on. The men ran beside it. At last they began to go down. The men caught a rabbit and ate it, giving Snowbird his part. Then they found more food. And at last they could get out of the wind and rest.

After a long time the men and the dog got to the Yukon river. There were people who gave them food. But Blacky was not with them.

This has been the story of how Snowbird grew up and became a great sled dog. But Snowbird's name was changed. The next story will tell you about Snowbird when his name was changed to Sandy.

Sandy

Big Mike was a man who took
the letters and packages from one
village in Alaska to another. He
had many fine sled dogs. For a
sled pulled by dogs was the only
way you could go from place to
place.

As soon as Big Mike saw
Snowbird he wanted to buy
him. He said he would give
Black Luke a lot of money for
his big dog with blue eyes. But
Black Luke would not sell
Snowbird.

Then Black Luke and Beaver found that they had to leave Alaska for a time. They had to go to the States to sell their furs. So they said that they would not sell Snowbird to Big Mike, but they would let him keep Snowbird for them until they got back.

But Big Mike had to say that he would be very good to Snowbird. And he had to say that he would never whip Snowbird. For Snowbird had never been whipped.

Big Mike changed Snowbird's name to Sandy, for the big dog's coat was turning a light yellow.

And "Sandy" was a much better name to call out when he called to his dogs as they pulled the sled.

Sandy was so big and strong that he was made the lead dog of Big Mike's team of sled dogs. The lead dog has to be very smart. He has to pick the way to go, for there are no roads over the snow. The lead dog has to keep all the other dogs pulling as they go after him.

Then, too, the lead dog has to keep the other dogs from fighting. Sandy was very big and strong, but he did not like to fight. When two of the sled dogs would start to fight, Sandy would watch them. Then, just at the right time, he would run at them and knock them both over. They would be so surprised that they would stop fighting.

There was one time when Sandy would not obey Big Mike. And Big Mike almost whipped Sandy.

It was almost the time of the "long night" when the sun hardly comes up at all. Big Mike was going across the hills to a village. It was a new trail for the man and his team.

It was almost dark when Sandy suddenly stopped and sat down. The dogs and sled stopped behind him.

"Mush," cried Big Mike. "Mush" means to go ahead. But Sandy sat there. He would not move.

The dogs had been going all day, and Big Mike thought that maybe the dogs were too tired. So Big Mike stopped for the night. He fed the dogs and camped right there.

In the morning, it was time to start, but it was still very dark. Big Mike wanted to get going on his way. He harnessed the dogs.

"Mush," cried Big Mike. But Sandy stood still. He would not go on.

Big Mike was very angry. This was the first time that Sandy had not obeyed him.

"Mush," cried Big Mike again. But Sandy did not move.

Then Big Mike took the whip from the back of the sled. It was so dark that he could hardly see Sandy at the head of the team of dogs. But Big Mike with his whip went up to where Sandy stood in the snow.

Just as Big Mike got to Sandy, his feet went from under him. He started to go down a steep hill that he had not seen.

Sandy jumped forward and got hold of Big Mike's coat with his teeth. He pulled back, and all the other dogs pulled back. They all seemed to know that they could all go down the hill.

The dogs pulled and pulled. Slowly Big Mike got back up the steep hill. He got to his feet.

After that, Big Mike always trusted Sandy.

The Race

Big Mike and his dog team had to go to Nome. At Nome, Big Mike found that there was going to be a big race. The best dogs from all Alaska had been brought to Nome for the race.

One of the men who was to have a team in the race was John Johnson, who was called the Iron Man because he was so strong. As soon as Johnson saw Sandy in Big Mike's team, he wanted to buy Sandy to be his lead dog in the race.

"Sandy is not my dog," said Big Mike. "I cannot sell him."

"I must have Sandy as my lead dog in the big race," said Johnson. "I will take good care of him. If you let me have him for the race, I will take care of all your dogs while you are in Nome."

At last, Big Mike let Johnson have Sandy to be his lead dog in the race.

The race was to be from Nome to a town called Candle. It was 408 miles in all. And there were to be eight teams in the race.

The day of the race, a blizzard began. But Sandy had gone

through many blizzards. Johnson's team was to go first. This was not good because the first team had to make the trail that the others could follow. But Johnson was not afraid. He was sure that he could keep ahead of the others.

"Mush," called Johnson, the Iron Man, and away the dogs went. On and on through the blizzard. On and on.

The race began at ten in the morning and the dogs ran all that day. Late in the afternoon, they had gone over 70 miles. Johnson let the dogs rest and fed them. Then they went on again through the snow. No one had caught up with them.

All night long the dogs kept going. Every few hours they would rest a few minutes. Johnson would go along the team and talk to each one, calling it by name. He would look at their feet to be sure they were not hurt.

Sandy seemed to know that every dog must run as fast as he could and keep on going. The dogs ran all next day. They rested now and then and were given something to eat. In the afternoon, they got to Candle ahead of all the other teams. But they had to have some rest.

The Iron Man went to sleep for four hours. When he woke up, he found that another team had come to Candle and had started back.

But Johnson took time to look over his dogs and to talk to them. He fed them and then harnessed them to the sled. Sandy was ready to go. But while Johnson did this, three more dog teams had got to Candle and had started back ahead of them.

When they were ready, "Mush,"

called the Iron Man, and they started off on the trail to Nome. This time they could follow the track of the other teams. But Johnson's team could not come up behind another team and go by them. If they did, the dogs would be sure to have a great fight. So when Johnson knew that a team was ahead of his, he told Sandy to make a new trail so that they could get around the other team and get ahead of them. This made the trail longer.

At last the Iron Man knew that he was ahead of all the other teams. Now they must keep ahead of them. All day and all night the dogs had run with just a few stops to rest and eat. The dogs were very tired. The Iron Man, who was so strong, was very tired too.

The blizzard was blowing harder. Johnson knew if he stopped again, the dogs were so tired that they would all go to sleep.

Sandy seemed to understand. He did not slow down. The Iron Man talked to his dogs. He could hardly see them, for his eyes were almost covered with snow.

Sandy ran on and on. The ice on the trail had cut his feet. He left red spots on the snow as he ran on and on.

Three days after they had started, the Iron Man and his team of dogs got back to Nome ahead of all the others. They had won the race.

Sandy, the lead dog, was now the most famous dog in Alaska. The papers told the story of the race. Black Luke, who had just come back from the States, was very happy. His dog came back to him, and they were together again.